3 DAY VEGAN

By Siovonne Smith

3 DAY VEGAN

... "The Better than Nothing Plan"

By Siovonne Smith

GOLDEN
GATE
PUBLISHERS

Dedicated to...

Those who inspire
or aspire to
a good and healthy life.

TABLE OF CONTENTS

Introduction: Pages 1-4
Why 3 Day Vegan?

Chapter 1: Pages 5-8
What is a Vegan?
What is a 3 Day Vegan?

Chapter 2: Pages 9-12
Why 3 Days?
Which 3 Days?

Chapter 3: Pages 13-16
My 3 Day Vegan test.

Chapter 4: Pages 17-20
3 Day Vegan Eating Plan.
Why Should I?
What are the Benefits?

Chapter 5: Pages 21-34
How to Start?
Why?
Sample Weekly Calendar.
First Week Exercise.

Chapter 6: Pages 35-48
What to Do?
First Week Preparations.
What to Expect During the First – Fourth Week.
What to Expect During the Fifth – Eighth Week.

Chapter 7: Pages 49-58
What are your Challenges and Obstacles?
Non-vegan foods hardest to give up.
Common Misconceptions.
Losing Weight as a 3 Day Vegan.
Flexibility as a 3 Day Vegan.
Traveling as a 3 Day Vegan.

TABLE OF CONTENTS

(Continued)

Chapter 8: Pages 59-64
Food Swaps and Substitutes.

Chapter 9: Pages 65-70
Cooking at Home.

Chapter 10: Pages 71-74
Eating as an Active Person or Athlete.

Chapter 11: Pages 75-78
Dining out as a 3 Day Vegan.

Chapter 12: Pages 79-82
What makes it easier?

Chapter 13: Pages 83-86
Treats to get you through.

Chapter 14: Pages 87-90
How your eating might change.

Chapter 15: Pages 91-102
Other activities to supplement your
3 Day Vegan Eating Plan.

Author Bio: Page 103
About the Author.

Why 3 Day Vegan?

Why write this book?

Possibly you, like me,
have been a bit curious about veganism.

Maybe you have vegan friends?

Maybe you've been reading about it?

Or seen something about it?

Maybe you even thought about giving it a try?

Maybe?

But for forever?

… I wasn't so sure.

Could I do it?

Did I want to?

Should I try?

Well…

Hmm…

Maybe for a day…

Or two?

Or maybe even three?

I could try... maybe... yes.

But…

How hard would this be?

And…

What are the challenges?

What are the benefits?

What can I eat?

What would I eat?

What about special events, holidays, or vacations?

I decided…

Let me do a test and see.

And…

Who's the guinea pig for this test?

Hmm…

I guess it's me.

"Our Crisis
Is Our Opportunity."

~ Siovonne Smith @TitleWordSmith

CHAPTER ONE:

What's a Vegan Anyway?

According to Merriam-Webster's Dictionary:

Vegan: a strict vegetarian who consumes no animal food or dairy products.

OK. So…

What's a 3 Day Vegan?

A 3 Day Vegan follows a vegan eating plan for three days a week.

Do I have to be a 3 Day Vegan?

Can I be Vegan for 1 or 2 days?

Or can I be a Full–time Vegan?

The answer is…

You can be whatever type of vegan you want to be.

This book, however, is geared towards those who want to try the vegan eating lifestyle on a more part-time basis; whether it be for 3 days, less, or maybe more.

For those who are interested in being a full-time vegan from the start there are many excellent books geared towards full-time veganism.

So why not just read full-time vegan books?

Because many people, whether it be for medical,
personal, or eating preferences,
choose not to be vegan on a full-time basis,
but yet might be curious nonetheless about the health
and environmental benefits of eating vegan,
and may be interested in trying it out…
possibly on a more temporary, flexible,
or continual part-time basis.

This book is also helpful for individuals as a possible precursor to being
a full-time vegan, or for those who want to begin and explore the vegan eating lifestyle
on a gradual, part-time basis first.

3 Day Vegan is also designed for full-time vegans who wish to share more
about their lifestyle with their family and friends…
possibly for those who have expressed some interest in veganism,
but yet are not quite sure how they would incorporate it into their daily lifestyle,
or if it could work for them.

This book takes into account different medical,
lifestyle, and other eating preferences
and requirements.

This book lets you design what's best for you
and gives you guidance on how you can do it.

To help you best succeed.

"Don't Wait for Opportunities...
Create Them."

~ Siovonne Smith @TitleWordSmith

TOP TIPS FROM CHAPTER 1:

3 Day Vegan is designed
to work with your lifestyle.

You're the boss!

**You design the plan
that's best for you.**

3 Day Vegan
... "The Better Than Nothing Plan"
gives you the tools you need
to help you best succeed.

CHAPTER TWO:

Why 3 Days?

I decided on 3 days because I thought I could do it, and
it would have a little more impact…

on my overall health,

and on the environment too.

It would create a little more consistency.

It would become part of my weekly routine.

This would result in eating vegan approximately 42% each week.

It seemed like "better than nothing".

So, I thought this would be a good start.

I didn't feel the need to do more.

… But that's me.

You can do whatever you want to do.

You can try one day to start if you prefer… or two?

Or maybe you want to do more than 3 days?

You choose what's right for you.

OK, so…

Which 3 Days?

Again, this is up to you.

For me I chose three consecutive days, Monday, Tuesday, and Wednesday.

The days don't have to be consecutive though.

It's whatever works best with your lifestyle.

I like having my Thursdays, Fridays, and weekends open
for different eating options.

However, if I have a special event on a Monday, Tuesday, or Wednesday,
and I don't want to follow the vegan eating plan on a given day,

I might switch my days.
And that's ok.

Because this plan is flexible
and designed by you,

to work with your life
... and your schedule too.

To help you best succeed.

TOP TIPS FROM CHAPTER 2:

Structure creates consistency.

Decide which days work best for you.

It's ok to be flexible.

"Flexibility Forces Fly."

~ Siovonne Smith @TitleWordSmith

CHAPTER THREE:

What Was My 3 Day Vegan Test?

To be a 3 Day Vegan for eight weeks.

Was I successful?

Yes!

What did I do?

I ate as a vegan for 3 days a week.

Was it easy?

No… not always, especially at the beginning.

Sometimes it took some extra willpower
and creativity

to find my best food-substitutes
or appropriate food options.

Did I need to think about food in more creative combinations?

Yes.

Have I discovered some new food options that I like?

Yes!

Have I continued being a 3 Day Vegan?

Yes.

How long have I been a 3 Day Vegan?

More than a year.

How can You do it?

Give it a try.

And…

See next chapters
for more details and tips on how to succeed.

TOP TIPS FROM CHAPTER 3:

Extra willpower may be needed at the start.

**It takes a little time
to get used to your new
3 Day Vegan eating lifestyle.**

Explore, be creative, and have fun!

CHAPTER FOUR:

3 Day Vegan Eating Plan

Why Should I?
What Are the Benefits of This Plan?

A large amount of research has been done over the years proving that eating fewer animal products, less animal fat, and eating more plant-based foods is not only better for your health, but also better for the environment.

A vegan eating plan may also reduce the risk or severity of major diseases such as, heart disease, high cholesterol, obesity, type 2 diabetes, as well as others.

A vegan eating plan may help with obtaining and maintaining a healthy weight.

A vegan eating plan may eliminate or reduce the need for medication.

Plant-based nutrition provides many valuable and necessary nutrients that you need daily, without harmful health or environmental effects.

Plant-based nutrition also uses less energy and environmental resources and causes less harm to the world overall.

And…

Nature is bountiful.

Whole foods are best.

Real food is where it's at.

And...

Do your best to stay away from pesticides,
lots of processed food,
and long lists of ingredients.

The fewer ingredients there are... the better.

And as they say... You are what you eat.

So, eat well, and be well.

Right?

Well... yes.

But...

Most of us already know these things... right?

Well... yes.

But... Sometimes it's hard to make healthy changes.

Well... yes.

Ok... so how do I start?

So glad you asked.

See next chapter...

TOP TIPS FROM CHAPTER 4:

Plant-based nutrition is good for you.

You are what you eat.

Less can be more.

CHAPTER FIVE:

HOW TO START?

First it should be noted that if you have any type of medical or dental needs, allergies, special requirements, or concerns, please speak with your doctor before starting this or any new eating plan.

Once all is ok and you are ready to start… here is the first step.

1. Keep track of how you usually eat for one week.

Why?

Because you need to know what your usual eating and drinking patterns are to create the most successful 3 Day Vegan Eating Plan.

The first week of this plan you will not change your normal eating style, just keep track of what you normally eat and drink.

This first week will help you determine your usual eating patterns so you can best understand what your obstacles might be in starting the 3 Day Vegan Eating Plan.

It will also help you determine which 3 days might be the best days for you to be a 3 Day Vegan.

(Please use sample chart on following page if desired.)

"There's No Better Time
Than Write Now."

~ Siovonne Smith @TitleWordSmith

TRACK YOUR EATING

TODAY'S DATE: _____

SUN	MON	TUE	WED	THU	FRI	SAT

**Breakfast
&
Water**

AM Snacks

**Lunch
&
Water**

PM Snacks

**Dinner
&
Water**

After Dinner
Drinks or Snacks

The exercise of
writing down how you usually eat,
during your first week,
will help you determine
your usual eating and drinking patterns,
so you can best understand
what your obstacles might be
in starting the
3 Day Vegan Eating Plan.

And...

It will also help you
determine which 3 days
are the best for you,
and your schedule,
to be a successful
3 Day Vegan.

To help you best succeed.

KEEP TRACK OF HOW YOU EAT

Choose From a Variety
of Fruits and Vegetables

First Week Exercise:

Keep a journal of what you eat and drink each day.

Write down your observations.

Do you normally eat red meat?

_____

If so… how often?

_____

Do you normally eat poultry?

_____

If so… how often?

_____

Do you normally eat seafood or shellfish?

_____

If so… how often?

_____

First Week Exercise:
(continued...)

Do you normally eat or drink dairy?

_____

If so… how often?

_____

Do you normally eat eggs?

_____

If so… how often?

_____

Do you normally eat a lot of processed foods?

_____

If so… how often?

_____

Do you normally eat a lot of junk food?

_____

If so… how often?

_____

And...

Do you usually read the ingredients on food labels?

_____

Do you notice how many calories?

_____

Or what type of protein you usually eat?

_____

And...

Do you normally eat a lot of vegetables?

_____

Or fruit?

_____

Or different types of whole grains?

_____

Or nuts?

_____

Do you drink water on a regular basis?

_____

And...

"Mix It Up."

~ Siovonne Smith @TitleWordSmith

Do you eat a wide range of foods?

_____

Do you eat fairly balanced?

_____

Do you get enough protein?

_____

Do you notice if something is organic or not?

_____

Processed or not?

_____

High in sugar or carbs?

_____

High in sodium content?

_____

OK then...

Now you know how you usually eat.

Now what?

"Brighten Someone's Day."

~ Siovonne Smith @TitleWordSmith

TOP TIPS FROM CHAPTER 5:

Take the first step.

If there are medical concerns clear with doctor.

Keep track...
Know your usual eating habits.

"Multicolor your Palette."

~ Siovonne Smith @TitleWordSmith

CHAPTER SIX:

Then... You Start.

How?

First pick the best 3 Days for you.

Which days would be easiest for you?
To give you the best chance for success.

Ok...
Do you have in mind your best 3 day options?

If so...
Choose those days to start.

Ok...
Now that you know your 3 Days...

Now what?

Write it Down

And...

Be Accountable to Yourself

Mark It Down!

MARCH | MARS | MARZO

SUNDAY DIMANCHE DOMINGO	MONDAY LUNDI LUNES	TUESDAY MARDI MARTES	WEDNESDAY MERCREDI MIÉRCOLES	THURSDAY JEUDI JUEVES

FEBRUARY

S	M	T	W	T	F	S
					1	2
3	4	5	6	7	8	9
10	11	12	13	14	15	16
17	18	19	20	21	22	23
24	25	26	27	28		

APRIL

S	M	T	W	T	F	S
	1	2	3	4	5	6
7	8	9	10	11	12	13
14	15	16	17	18	19	20
21	22	23	24	25	26	27
28	29	30				

		Mardi Gras	Ash Wednesday Cendres Miércoles de Ceniza	
3	4	5	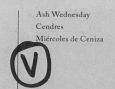 6	7 •
Daylight Saving Time Begins (US, Canada) 10	11	12	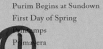 13	14 ☽
Saint Patrick's Day 17	18	19	Purim Begins at Sundown First Day of Spring Printemps Primavera 20	21 ○
24 Summer Time Begins (EU) Mothering Sunday (UK) 31	25	26	27	28 ☾

Ok... How?

First note your vegan days down somewhere.

What do you mean exactly?

Write down the days you have chosen to be vegan so you don't forget each week.

In the beginning it will be something
you will need to remember
and remind yourself of, because
it won't be second nature yet.

What did I do?

I have a large calendar hanging in my kitchen.

At first, I wrote a big V
with a circle around it
in a thick blue felt pen,
on the days that I was vegan each week.

I originally did this to remind myself,
and to help me keep track.

I continued doing this for approximately the first six months.

Anything Else Help?

Yes.

What?

Share With Others.

Share with those you live with,
or typically eat out with,
the days you are a 3 Day Vegan.

Then others can share
in your journey
with you,
or be there to support you,
and also remind you,
if you ever forget.

And...

Help Others Too.

If others are joining you
on their own 3 Day Vegan journey,
you can also help and support them.

"Help out others when you can...
We all need a little help."

~ Siovonne Smith @TitleWordSmith

What's Next?

Prepare!

Get Started!

Have Fun!

First Week:
What to expect the first week?

The first week may be the biggest challenge
since everything will be different and new.

It will be important to think back on your first test week,
and remember your typical eating and drinking patterns,
and plan accordingly for possible food substitutes.

Before you start… Go shopping.

Buy vegan appropriate food and beverages
that are great substitutes for your usual food and drinking patterns.

What Else?

Buy more fruits and vegetables.

If you don't have one already, put a big bowl on your kitchen or dining room table,
and fill it with fruit and vegetables that you like.

Fruit, and vegetables too, will be an easy snack to grab
if you see it every time you walk by the fruit and vegetable bowl.

Anything besides fruit and vegetables?

Yes.

Special Treats:

Incorporate some special vegan treats into the first week, such as vegan
non-dairy ice cream bars with or without chocolate, vegan gummy bears,
popcorn, licorice, or any other vegan treats you like.

What about Restaurants?

When you're in a restaurant or café
scan the menu for what could work.

If you can't find much on the menu, talk to the restaurant staff about
possible substitutes, or acceptable food options.

Most restaurant staff members that I've encountered on my 3 Day Vegan journey
have been eager to help me find something that they think I would like.

Important Tips to Remember:

Make it Fun!
Make it Delicious!

And…
Don't Forget:

You can still indulge in many of your old favorite delicious treats as a vegan, or make new ones.

There are many tasty options out there.

Check out your local market or farmers market for a range of options.

Markets that specialize in organic or vegetarian options are good starting points.

First - Fourth Week:

What to expect during the first - fourth week?

During this time you will experiment with different vegan food and drinking options.

You will start to get the "hang of it" by the fourth week. It won't be second nature quite yet, but you will have figured out many options that will work for you.

Possibly you'll have your new vegan choices all lined up, or will try food options, maybe for the first time, and then determine your favorites.

Once you have some favorites, you might switch off between different vegan options throughout the week.

You'll probably be getting used to your vegan milk and vegan dairy type products, and will most likely have discovered some brands of products that you like, and will now frequently choose those items in your local grocery store or farmer's market when you go shopping.

You'll also likely research and discover some new favorite markets, cafés or restaurants, that you can rely on for some good vegan food choices.

You might feel that certain times are still a challenge when choosing your vegan options, because this is still a new experience.

You might anticipate and look forward to your non-vegan days.

Fifth - Eighth Week:

What to expect during the fifth - eighth week?

At this point being a 3 Day Vegan will start becoming a regular part of your routine.

You might not even have to remind yourself that it's a vegan day,
on your given 3 Day Vegan days.

Your favorite foods and food substitutes are now part of your regular
eating routine for your vegan days.

You might even find yourself eating vegan food
options on non-vegan days,
just because you want to, have it available,
or prefer it sometimes.

You will most likely have some favorite dishes on a regular rotation,
whether it be cooking at home, or dining out.

Your family and friends will be getting more used to your
new 3 Day Vegan eating lifestyle as well.

Some of your family, friends, or colleagues, might also become
interested in the 3 Day Vegan lifestyle, and might want to try it too.

You might start to look forward to your vegan days
when your non-vegan days are over.

"We Are All Students."

~ Siovonne Smith @TitleWordSmith

TOP TIPS
FROM CHAPTER 6:

FIRST WEEK:

Be accountable; keep track and tell others.

Buy lots of fruit and vegetables.

Ask for vegan suggestions in markets and restaurants.

FIRST – FOURTH WEEK:

You'll start to get more used to your 3 Day Vegan Eating Plan.

Experiment with new food options.

You'll discover new foods, markets, cafés and restaurants, that suit your new 3 Day Vegan eating lifestyle.

FIFTH – EIGHTH WEEK:

Expect that each week will be a little different.

Explore new vegan-friendly cuisines.

You might look forward to returning to your vegan days.

"Life's like driving a clutch…
don't be afraid to roll."

~ Siovonne Smith @TitleWordSmith

CHAPTER SEVEN:

WHAT ARE YOUR CHALLENGES?

WHAT ARE YOUR OBSTACLES?

What are the non-vegan foods you think would be the hardest to give up?

Milk
Yogurt
Butter
Ice cream
Other Dairy
Eggs

Seafood
Shellfish
Poultry
Other White Meat
Red Meat

Processed foods containing non-vegan foods,
such as some cakes, cookies, pies, crackers, breads, or other food items.

What are the non-vegan drinks you think would be the hardest to give up?

Milk
Milk-based tea, coffee, and espresso drinks
Milkshakes

WHAT ABOUT
COMMON MISCONCEPTIONS?

Will I Lose Weight as a Vegan?
Isn't Vegan Food LoCal?

Not necessarily.

Vegan food can be high in fat or calories, depending on what you eat, and how much.

Coconut milk, although delicious, is higher in fat.
It's still a good item to incorporate into your vegan days
on occasion, but just pay attention, and keep it in moderation.

Nuts are also very nutritious and delicious,
but can be high in fat, depending on the types of nuts,
and also depending on how much you eat.
So, again, they should be kept in moderation.

Avocados are also delicious, but should be kept in moderation.

I've also noticed many vegan options (in restaurants, and sometimes in recipes too)
include more sauces, or other items, that may include more sodium.

Pay attention to that.

Ask for your sauce(s) on the side whenever possible.

Is it possible to gain weight?

It's possible…

if you don't pay attention
to extra sodium, sugar, or the quantity of higher fat foods such as:

nuts, avocado, non-dairy and coconut milk based products,
or toppings and sauces that may include
more sodium than what you're used to.

Pay attention to your sodium and sugar consumption.

If you start consuming more sodium,
sugar, or other sweeteners,
that may pose a potential problem.

It's always a good idea to check labels and keep things simple; the less ingredients the better.

Know what's in your food.

And...

Understand the food ingredients that are listed on the nutrition label.

But...
Is it Also Possible to Lose Weight
as a 3 Day Vegan?

Yes… It's possible.

By eliminating animal products and animal fat from your diet 3 Days a Week,
you should be consuming less fat and possibly less calories,
which will make it easier to lose weight,
if that is your desire.

But it's still important to pay attention
to portion sizes and timing of when you eat.

Don't Eat Too Late and Watch Portions.

In general try not to eat too late in the evening, and do your best to stop eating
when you feel well satisfied, but not quite full.

What about special occasions?

There might be special events such as parties, events, or holidays,
that you prefer to go non-vegan.

What to Do?

It's ok to be flexible.

You can give yourself the option to review and eat the vegan options,
if they exist at your special occasion, or swap a vegan meal for a non-vegan meal.
Later you can swap a non-vegan meal for a vegan meal to even things out.

Or…

If you don't want to be vegan that day?

That's ok…

You can switch your days.

Or…
You can pro-rate meals in advance, or after.

For example, if you typically eat 3 meals a day,
then you can eat 3 vegan meals in advance,
to work with your schedule, to make up for your regular vegan day.

If it's for more than one vegan day,
then multiply the amount of days by 3,
for a correct assessment of how many meals you should pro-rate in advance,
to compensate for your usually scheduled vegan days.

What About Traveling?

Traveling can sometimes be a challenge,
especially when you're just beginning
your 3 Day Vegan journey.

A couple of months after starting my 3 Day Vegan adventure
I traveled to Argentina, not a country known for its vegan lifestyle.

On the contrary, it's quite famous for its meat or "carne".

So, what to do?

Claim Traveler's Dispensation

You may have already heard this term if you ever attended religious services regularly.

What does Traveler's Dispensation usually mean?

It often means... Skipping services while on vacation.

Ok… so, I can skip my vegan days on vacation?

Whatever you do is up to you.

I decided it was ok,
while on vacation, if I needed or wanted to.

In other words, at times, I would claim "Traveler's Dispensation" while on vacation if I choose to.

But I also decided to scope out what the vegan options might be
while on vacation too.

In truth, during my traveling time in Argentina, I did not find a lot of vegan options,
although I did find some vegan options on occasion.

So, I did my best to adjust. I found that I did make a couple of vegan swaps
during my vacation here and there,
although I did not officially do my 3 Day Vegan days
while on vacation in Argentina.

When I returned from vacation though,
I decided to add a few extra vegan days
to my first week back.

It's not necessary, but I wanted to give it a try.

In the end, it's whatever works for you.

Following Argentina, I also had some vacation time in New York City,
and I found there were more vegan options on this trip.

In addition I also banked
a couple of extra vegan days
before I left,
and decided to check-out the available
vegan options, whenever possible,
while I was there.

I was happily surprised to see some great vegan options at my hotel,
as well as in my NYC neighborhood, as well as in other parts of the city too.

But regardless of how much you do
or don't do,
(of your usual vegan routine)
while on vacation,
it's important to get back to
your normal eating routine
once you return home.

This will help keep things as seamless as possible,
and maintain the strengths and benefits you've gained
while being a 3 Day Vegan.

TOP TIPS FROM CHAPTER 7:

Anticipate obstacles.

Being vegan
does not guarantee losing weight.

Claim "Traveler's Dispensation"
while traveling... if you want to.

"Strength Comes From Within."

~ Siovonne Smith @TitleWordSmith

"Defy your Expectations."

~ Siovonne Smith @TitleWordSmith

CHAPTER EIGHT:

FOOD SWAPS

... IT'S ALL ABOUT THE SUBSTITUTES.

What are some great substitutes for dairy?

Plant-based milk
or plant-based dairy products
including:

Almond, Soy, Cashew, Oats,
and Coconut-based.

Plant-based ice cream
or sorbet.

Plant-based butter products.

Avocado in place of cheese
or butter.

It's also important to eat enough protein
on your vegan days.

What are some great substitutes for Meat,
Poultry, and Seafood?

There are many vegan meat substitutes in your local markets and restaurants,
including a variety of grains, fruits, vegetables, seeds, nuts, or beans.

Some may include:

Portobello and Other Mushrooms

Eggplant

"The Impossible Burger"

Varieties of Beans

Chickpeas, Hummus

Nuts or Nut-based Butters

Lentils and Lentil-based Foods

Jackfruit

Seitan

Tofu

Tempeh

Fruits and Vegetables

Egg Substitutes:

Tofu, Tempeh, Flax seeds, and Chia Seeds

There may also be non-egg substitutes available in your local market.
Ask your local grocer. Or... substitute another vegan food item.

Herbs & Spices:

Add fresh or dried herbs and spices to your food for added flavor.

Good Things to Incorporate

Note: As long as you don't have an allergy, medical, or dental reason to avoid any specific food items, nuts, whether whole or chopped up into smaller pieces, are an excellent food group to incorporate into your daily eating plan, on vegan and non-vegan days.

Brazil Nuts To Me = Dose of Serenity

Brazil nuts, which contain the important but not commonly found mineral selenium, are an excellent food choice to incorporate into your daily eating routine.

I normally eat two Brazil nuts each morning.

Two Brazil nuts every day would satisfy most people's selenium requirements.

Most types of nuts are fantastic to include as part of your daily eating routine…
such as almonds, walnuts, and many others too.

Almonds are an excellent source of calcium and protein.
Walnuts provide protein, zinc, Vitamin E, and folate.

Note:
All nuts have health benefits,
so they are an excellent option... and delicious too,
to experiment with and to try the many different varieties.

TOP TIPS FROM CHAPTER 8:

It's all about the food swaps.

Incorporate enough protein
into your vegan days.

Be versatile and creative
in choosing food options.

"Stay Curious."

~ Siovonne Smith @TitleWordSmith

CHAPTER NINE:

COOKING AT HOME

WHAT YOU MIGHT REDISCOVER
IN THE KITCHEN.

As an adventurer I've always loved different food cuisines and food combinations.

Being a 3 Day Vegan
allows me to experiment with different food variations
whether I am eating at home or away from home.

Delicious & Nutritious

I've discovered many excellent vegan cookbooks
during my 3 Day Vegan adventure,
and I'm continually amazed at all the delicious and healthy eating options.

Just looking at some of the delicious recipes gave me
hope and inspiration that I would be able to find or make
many enjoyable, as well as nutritional,
vegan eating options.

Because Eating to Me =

Nutrition + Enjoyment

I need and want to enjoy my eating experience whenever possible

… Probably you too.

And when you are cooking for yourself
you can experiment even more,
and choose your favorite ingredients
and textures that you prefer.

You might discover or rediscover your local farmers market
or local store,
and find that it carries many organic and vegan options.

You might even share some
of your favorite recipes
with your family and friends,
and introduce them to the possibilities
of a vegan or 3 Day Vegan eating lifestyle.

The possibilities are endless,
and you are the chef.

Experiment
and Have Fun!

"Challenge Comfort Zone."

~ Siovonne Smith @TitleWordSmith

TOP TIPS FROM CHAPTER 9:

You are the chef de cuisine.

Food should be nutritious and delicious.

Enjoy cooking at home with new recipes
and food options.

CHAPTER TEN:

EATING AS AN ACTIVE PERSON OR ATHLETE

Being active is an important part of any health plan.

If you are an active person,
with a regular exercise program, as I am,
it's also important to give yourself enough of the nutrients
that you need for your active lifestyle.

You may have to pay extra attention to make sure you get enough protein
on your vegan and non-vegan days.

It's beneficial to incorporate enough protein
into your daily eating plan as an active person or athlete.

And to make sure you consume an adequate
amount of needed nutrients and vitamins.

And to drink enough water.

Your food should nourish your muscles,
feed your soul, and tantalize your taste-buds too...
for a complete and fulfilling eating experience.

Choose From A Variety
of Vegan Protein Sources

"Positivity Percolating."

~ Siovonne Smith @TitleWordSmith

TOP TIPS FROM CHAPTER 10:

Be Active.

**Incorporate enough protein
for your active lifestyle.**

Drink enough water.

CHAPTER ELEVEN:

DINING OUT AS A 3 DAY VEGAN.

How about when you go to a restaurant?

How hard would that be?

As someone who likes to go out on a regular basis,
whether it be to a café or a restaurant,
I have experimented frequently with how to be
a 3 Day Vegan while dining out.

You'll probably discover new food options
that you may have overlooked before.

Sometimes you will speak to the restaurant staff
about what they would recommend.

You might even offer your own suggestions
or recommendations to the restaurant staff,
or ask if the restaurant can change a menu item slightly,
so that it works for you.

Frequently you'll scan the menu
to see what the restaurant usually offers, or has available,
and then if needed, possibly propose a new item,
with their on-hand ingredients, to eat on that day,
or possibly to add to their menu,
on a more permanent basis.

I have been guilty of all of the above and more.

What I find is that often restaurants are very open
to accommodating what I would like,
if they have the ingredients on site.

Sometimes they might add a new menu option
to their permanent menu from a suggestion.

Or I'll meet restaurant staff who express interest
in trying out the vegan lifestyle, or are already vegan,
and then they want to assist me,
in finding some good menu options.

I find that most restaurant staff
are usually encouraging
of my vegan eating attempts
while dining out.

Food options you may rediscover as a 3 Day Vegan:

There are some foods or food options that you may rediscover because of their vegan friendly options.

Many of these items can be nutritionally enhanced with vegetables, fruits, nuts, herbs and spices, or other vegan friendly food options.

Some potential "oldy but goody" comfort foods:

Pasta (Some are vegan, some are not... check label)
Ramen Noodles (without non-vegan items)
Rice Dishes (without non-vegan items)
Peanut Butter and Other Nut Butters

As well as:

Bagels (Some are vegan, some are not... check label)
Licorice
Popcorn (without non-vegan items)
Dill Pickles
Frozen Ice Treats (without non-vegan items),
including popsicles and sorbet.

And...
Many Asian and International cuisine options
(without non-vegan items).

And...
Options in Food Courts in Shopping Centers
(Which typically offer a wide variety of cuisines,
including some possible vegan options).

TOP TIPS FROM CHAPTER 11:

Dining out can sometimes be a challenge,
(especially in the beginning)
but it can also be fun to discover
new vegan restaurant options.

**Talk to restaurant staff
about your needs.**

Rediscover some old favorite foods
that were vegan all along.

CHAPTER TWELVE:

WHAT MAKES IT EASIER?

Any new eating plan
will take a little time
to adjust to.

Sometimes
it will not seem easy.

What helps along the way?

Talk to people
about your new eating journey.

Sometimes
others have great vegan eating suggestions
or recommendations.

Sometimes others are thinking about
eating in a new way too...
but do not know how to do it.

Be open to recommendations
and different cuisines.

Sometimes a restaurant
that hears about your new eating plan
may offer some great eating suggestions
of items that are already on their menu,
or create something special
just for you.

Sometimes restaurants may add
more vegan eating options permanently
after hearing about your "3 Day Vegan" journey.

Sometimes discovering new eating options
is fun, exciting, and creative!

Sometimes eating as a vegan
makes you feel a little more fit and healthy.

Sometimes you might feel
that your clothes fit a little better.

TOP TIPS FROM CHAPTER 12:

**Talk with others about your
3 Day Vegan journey.**

Be open to new foods.

Enjoy the benefits.

CHAPTER THIRTEEN:

TREATS TO GET YOU THROUGH

Let's face it.
Sometimes we all need a treat
to get us through the rough days.

We want to eat delicious and nutritious food. Right?

And...

Sometimes... maybe even something that seems
just a little bit indulgent or special too.

So... what are some great
vegan treat options?

You mean besides delicious fruit that's in season?

We already know about that one
... right?

Here are some more ideas:

Plant-based ice cream and sorbet products

Coconut or other non-dairy based ice cream bars with chocolate

Vegan pizza

Vegan gummy bears

Vegan licorice

Popcorn
(make sure no added non-vegan butter or other products)

Chips
(make sure no added non-vegan products)

Vegan pies, vegan cakes, vegan brownies, and vegan cookies

Fruit and plant-based non-dairy smoothies

Coffee or Tea drinks with vegan plant-based dairy products

Special fruit-based or other sparkling waters
(many without added sodium)

Fun juice drinks

Nut and dried fruit packs

Dried fruit

Vegan trail mix packs

TOP TIPS FROM CHAPTER 13:

Sometimes you need a treat.

You'll discover new delicious vegan desserts
and celebratory types of foods.

Ask others for vegan suggestions
and recommendations.

CHAPTER FOURTEEN:

HOW YOUR EATING MIGHT CHANGE ON NON-VEGAN DAYS:

After you've been a 3 Day Vegan
for a little while
you will find that you are looking
at potential vegan options,
even on your non-vegan days.

Some days you might be a half-day vegan,
without even realizing it.

Or you might make or order a vegan
and non-vegan dish,
just because you want to know
what the vegan dish is like,
for future reference.

You are now open
to more food options.

Some days you may find that
even though you are not vegan
on a specific given day,
you might still find that
you are frequently vegetarian.

But it's whatever you want.

Because this plan
needs to work for you.

For you to have
your best chance of success.

So… you're the boss!

You design your optimal plan,
and do what's best for you!

TOP TIPS FROM CHAPTER 14:

You're the boss.

You might find that you choose
vegan items
on your non-vegan days.

Enjoy your journey,
and design the plan that
offers you the best chance of success.

CHAPTER FIFTEEN:

OTHER ACTIVITIES TO SUPPLEMENT YOUR 3 DAY VEGAN EATING PLAN.

Fit = Fabulous

Strong = Super

EXERCISE

Exercise indoors or outdoors
(in nature whenever possible).

No matter your current activity level,
it's important to be active.

Do more than you usually do,
but begin slowly.

For example;
If your idea of exercise
is getting off the couch to get something
out of the refrigerator,
then take things slowly and build up.

Begin by taking walking laps
around your house or apartment
... then later around the block, your neighborhood,
or around the nearby track.

If you are a serious athlete,
then mix up your workouts
and routine with a little more variety,
in order to challenge your comfort zone,
and build new muscle and strength.

If you're somewhere in between;
maybe someone doing a little bit of exercise,
but not quite a serious athlete,
then start by taking an exercise class or two,
or start a walking or jogging routine
(by yourself, with a friend, or with a group of friends).
(Clear with doctor first, if needed.)

And if you're interested in strength training...

Start an easy and safe weight-lifting routine, slowly,
to build up strength.

Make sure you're supervised
by an appropriate trainer or gym staff member
when you begin or start any new weight-training program
to prevent possible injuries.

Another fun way to exercise?

Take a dance class or simply...

Dance to Some Music.

And, or...

Do Some Stretching Work.

Such as on your own in the living room,
on the beach, at the lake, or along the river.

Or take a stretching, yoga, or pilates class,
either in person, online, or on TV.

BREATH WORK

It's important to breathe properly.

And…

Certain activities will help, like yoga,
or doing special breathing exercises.

Check out your local gym for classes
teaching breathing exercises, yoga,
or other exercise classes
that offer health benefits.

Most gyms offer classes for all levels.

Or for a quick and easy breathing technique…

Take 3 Deep Breaths
(inhale, and then exhale)
when feeling
any type of stress,
as an instant stress reliever.

In addition, there's also…

MEDITATION

Meditation may include
prayer, being still,
and thinking positive mantras.

There are many books on how to meditate.

Or…

You can choose to sit still,
with eyes open or closed,
for five minutes or more each day,
and either just listen to the stillness around you,
or think about a positive mantra.

Or…

While you walk, bike,
jog, run, or take the dog for a stroll,
pay attention to your surroundings,
and look, listen, and enjoy
the scents and scenes of nature.

BE PRESENT AND ENJOY THE MOMENT!

Also...

KINDNESS

Be kind to yourself
in learning and discovering
what works for you in your journey.

Also, be kind to others
with their journey.

Kindness makes the world
a better place.

And...

LIVE LIFE
IN GOOD HEALTH,
JOY,
KINDNESS,
AND...

TO YOUR FULL
AND AMAZING POTENTIAL!

TOP TIPS FROM CHAPTER 15:

**Supplement your 3 Day Vegan lifestyle
with healthy exercises
and stress reducing activities.**

Be kind with yourself and others.

Live life to your full potential.

"Find Inspiration in Nature."

~ Siovonne Smith @TitleWordSmith

"Design your Destiny."

~ Siovonne Smith @TitleWordSmith

ABOUT THE AUTHOR

Siovonne Smith...

Writer, explorer, and adventurer,
has been interested in nutrition from an early age.

How nutrition helps people achieve optimal health
and provides amazing benefits,
while sometimes eliminating
or reducing the effects of disease
or the need for medicine is especially fascinating.

Besides an interest in nutrition,
Siovonne is creative, curious, and a continual learner.
She also writes poems, stories, and screenplays.

Follow her writing, updates, and creativity
on ✔ @TitleWordSmith,
or check out
www.TitleWordSmith.com.

For more on "3 Day Vegan"
check out www.3DayVegan.com.

"We All Have A Story."

~ Siovonne Smith @TitleWordSmith